BASTIEN PIANO BASICS
PIANO

LEVEL 2

BY JAMES BASTIEN

KJOS NEIL A. KJOS MUSIC COMPANY • SAN DIEGO, CALIFORNIA

Dear teachers and parents:

Piano, Level 2 presents important new information for the student. The learning sequence is carefully graded to assure steady progress, while the full-color illustrations entertain and reinforce along the way. The selection of pieces includes original works as well as familiar folk songs and pop styles in creative, enjoyable arrangements.

The companion books—**Theory** and **Performance**—are coordinated page-by-page (see *Contents*) to provide thorough reinforcement of basic concepts. The **Bastien Music Flashcards** may be assigned for extra drill in learning notes, key signatures, music signs, and terms. The **Bastien Music Notebook**, an assignment book, may be used throughout the series.

BASTIEN PIANO BASICS is a method designed for achievement and success. We offer you our best wishes for the rich rewards music can bring to each child's life.

Neil A. Kjos Music Company
James Bastien
Jane Smisor Bastien

ISBN 0-8497-5267-1

Contents

*To reinforce the feeling of achievement, the teacher or student may put a √ when the page has been mastered.

© 1985 Kjos West

4

Binary Form

This piece is in **binary,** or **two-part** form.
The two parts are called Sections A and B.

Clap Hands

Mexican Folk Song

WP202

July 2nd!   ♩=66 with m   15 mins.

no break, prepare earlier

Section B

⑤ F chord (Broken Form)

⑤ C chord

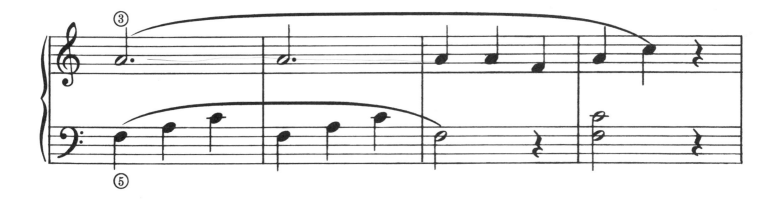

⑤

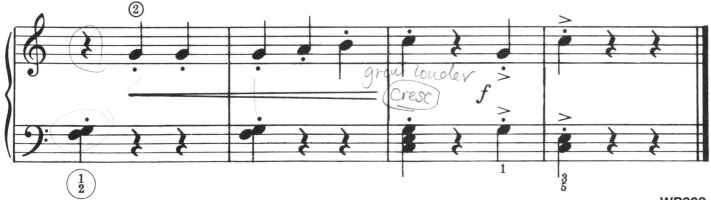

grow louder
cresc   f

Half Step

A **half step** is the distance from one key to the very next key, with **no key between.**

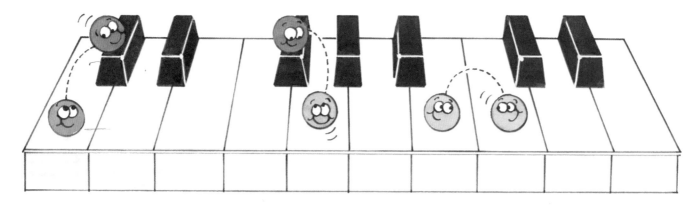

Play these half steps.

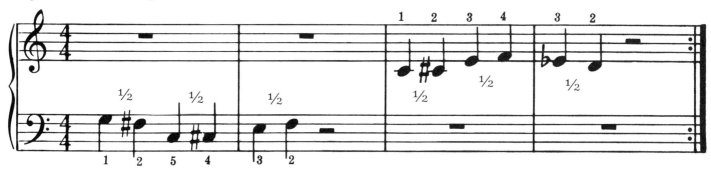

Whole Step

A **whole step** is the distance from one key to the next key, with **one key between.**

Play these whole steps.

Major Scale

A **Major scale** has eight tones formed in a pattern of whole and half steps.
The scale is divided into two equal parts, each having four notes. Each part is called a **tetrachord.** The pattern for each tetrachord is

whole step (1), **whole step** (1), **half step** (½).

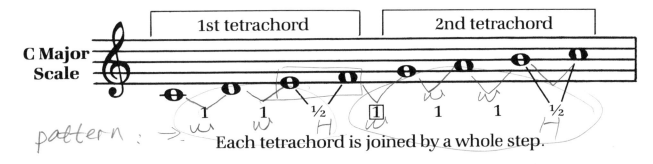

pattern: → w w H w 1 1 H

Each tetrachord is joined by a whole step.

Warm-ups

Play each of these scale warm-ups several times a day.

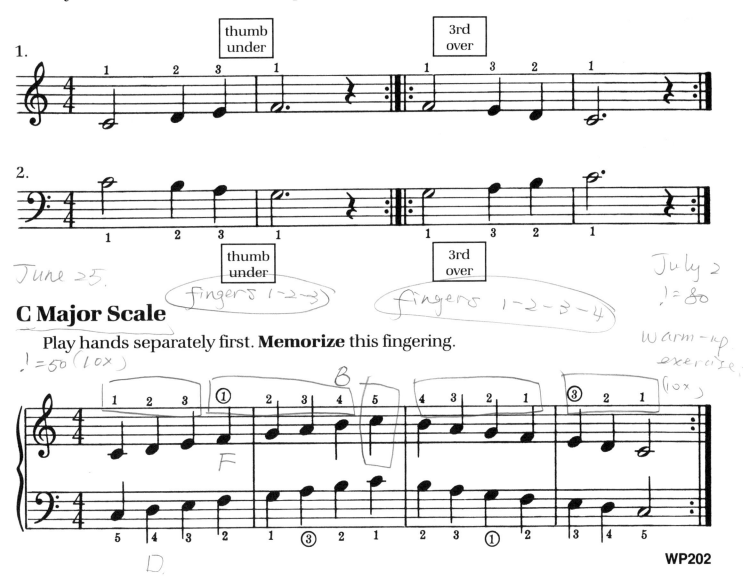

June 25.

thumb under — fingers 1-2-3
3rd over — fingers 1-2-3-4

July 2
♩=80

Warm-up exercise
(10x)

C Major Scale

Play hands separately first. **Memorize** this fingering.

♩=50 (10x)

WP202

Scaling the Rockies

Moderato

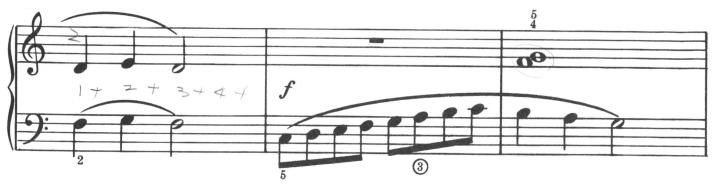

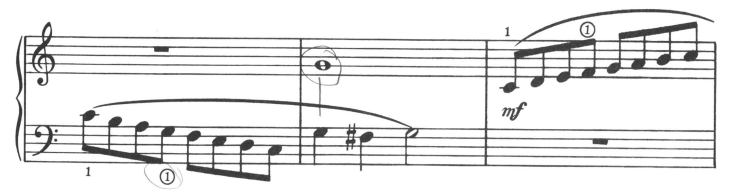

Ternary Form

This piece is in **ternary,** or **three-part** form.
The three parts are called Sections **A, B, A.**

Carnival

6th

[handwritten: size: unison → same note   4th, 5th, 6th, 7th]
[handwritten: 2nd → step,]
[handwritten: 3rd → skip   Octave → 8 notes]

[handwritten: there is a gap between finger 1 & 2]

[handwritten: Then, your fingers 1-5 will play an 6th interval.]

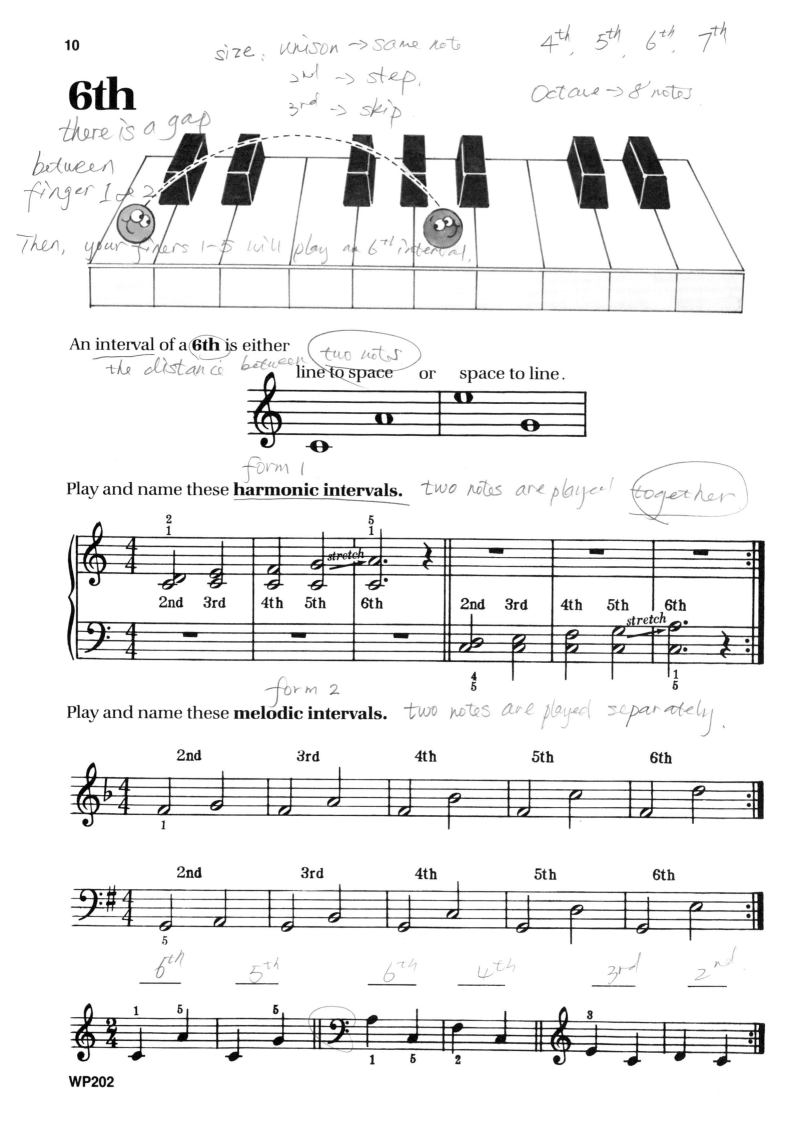

An interval of a **6th** is either *[handwritten: the distance between]* (two notes) line to space   or   space to line.

[handwritten: form 1]

Play and name these **harmonic intervals.** *[handwritten: two notes are played (together)]*

2nd   3rd   4th   5th   6th   2nd   3rd   4th   5th   6th

[handwritten: form 2]

Play and name these **melodic intervals.** *[handwritten: two notes are played separately.]*

2nd   3rd   4th   5th   6th

2nd   3rd   4th   5th   6th

[handwritten: 6th   5th   6th   4th   3rd   2nd]

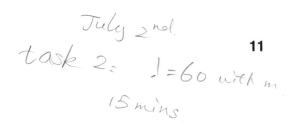

task 1:

Draw a circle around the melodic 6ths.

Harmonic Blues

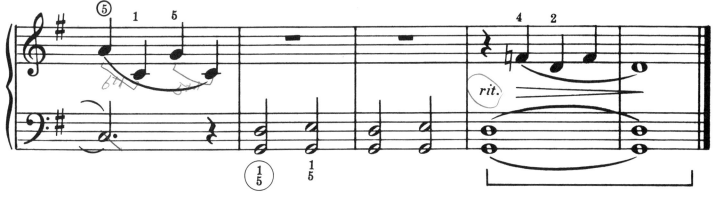

5th and 6th Warm-up

Play as written, then **transpose** (play in a key different than what is written) to the keys of F and G.

Play as written, then transpose to F and G.

Skip to My Lou

July 9

Lively

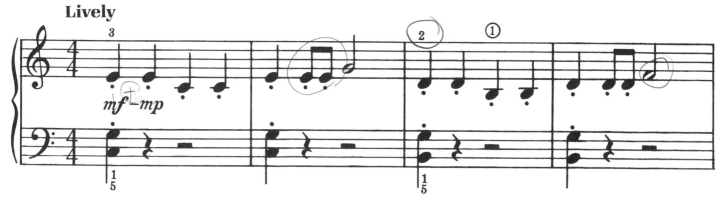

Draw a circle around the 6ths.

Moonlight Mist

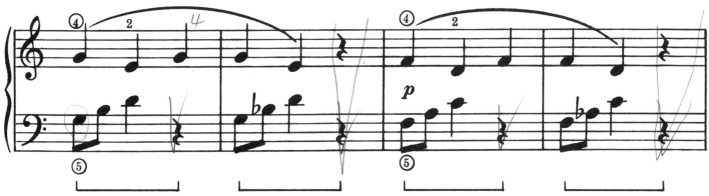

7th

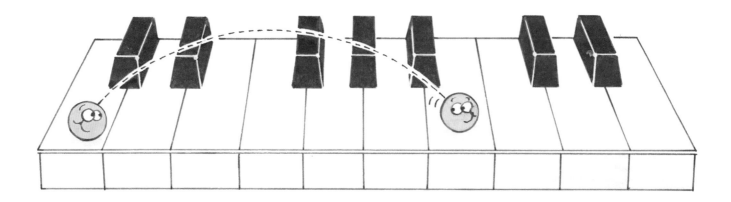

An interval of a **7th** is either (line to line) or space to space.

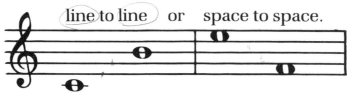

Play and name these **harmonic intervals**.

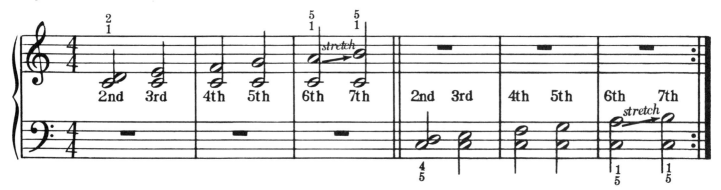

Play and name these **melodic intervals.**

First ending **Second ending**

1. Play first time through, then repeat the section. 2. Play second time through, omitting first ending.

Draw a circle around the 7ths.

In the Ocean Deep

Moderato

New note D

Primary Chords

Chords built on the first, fourth, and fifth degrees of the scale are called **primary chords.**

Each chord has a Roman numeral: I, IV, V.
Each chord has a name:

first note

I chord = **tonic** chord
IV chord = **subdominant** chord
V chord = **dominant** chord

Play these primary chords in C Major.

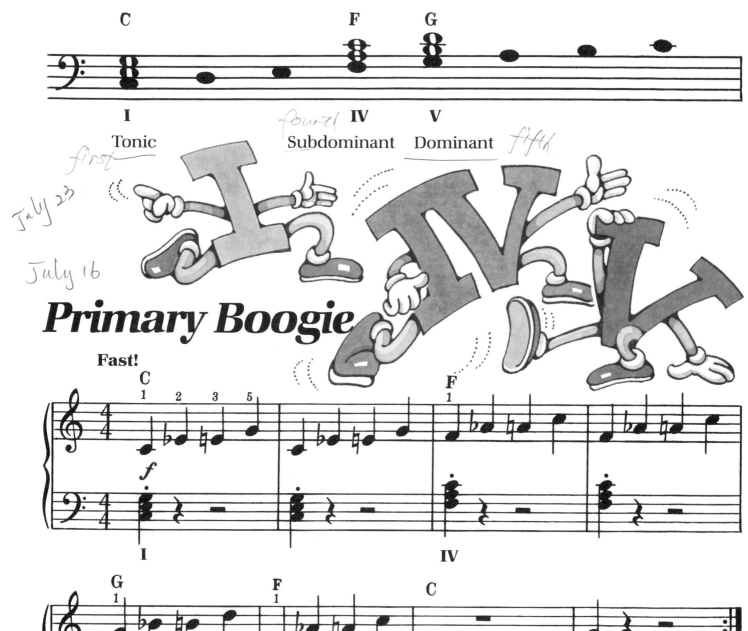

Tonic   Subdominant   Dominant

Primary Boogie

July 16

Write the chord names above the R.H.

Shooting the Rapids

July 23.

Lively

I   IV   I

V   IV   I

go back to beginning
and repeat until
D. C. al Fine
Fine

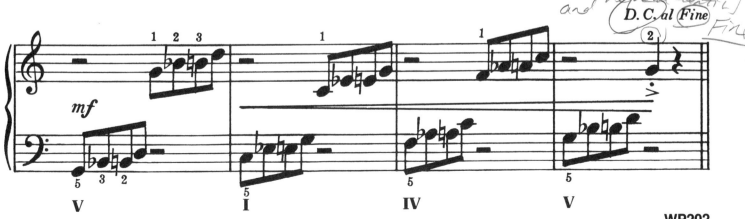

V   I   IV   V

August 13. H.T.

Triads and Inversions

A **triad** (a three-note chord) in **root position** looks like this:

line   line   line   5th   3rd   Root

space   space   space   5th   3rd   Root

An **inversion** is a different arrangement of the notes in a triad:

Root position   1st inversion   2nd inversion

Note: The root is the **top** note of the 4th in an inversion.

July 16

5x. August

R.H. → whole piece
L.H. → whole piece

Play the L.H. alone. Play the R.H. alone one octave higher than written. Play slowly and listen to the sound of each chord.

Turning Cartwheels

New note E

New note F

Chord Progression I IV

A **chord progression** is a change from one chord to another.
The chord progression I IV is easier to play by playing the IV chord in its
2nd inversion. By using the inversion for the IV chord the hand can
stay in place rather than moving to play root position chords.

Warm-up

Practice this **chord progression** in C Major. Play by "feel,"
without looking at your hand for the chord changes.

Rock!

August 6.

Steady rock beat

Chord Progression I V7

The complete V7 chord in root position has four notes.
The V7 chord is built on the fifth scale degree.

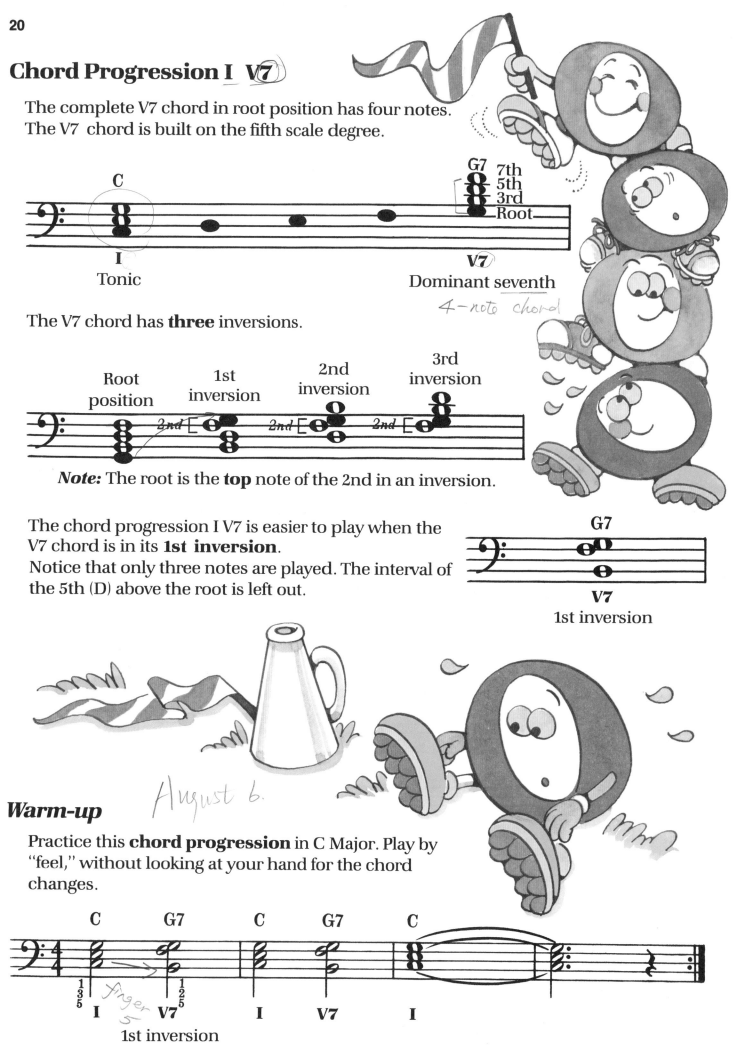

C
I
Tonic

G7 7th
5th
3rd
Root
V7
Dominant seventh

4-note chord

The V7 chord has **three** inversions.

Root position   1st inversion   2nd inversion   3rd inversion

Note: The root is the **top** note of the 2nd in an inversion.

The chord progression I V7 is easier to play when the V7 chord is in its **1st inversion**.
Notice that only three notes are played. The interval of the 5th (D) above the root is left out.

G7
V7
1st inversion

Warm-up

August 6.

Practice this **chord progression** in C Major. Play by "feel," without looking at your hand for the chord changes.

C   G7   C   G7   C

1
3
5
I   finger 5   V7   1st inversion   I   V7   I

1
2
5

Mary Ann

Moderato

Calypso Song

Chord Progression I   IV   V7

Primary chords in root position:

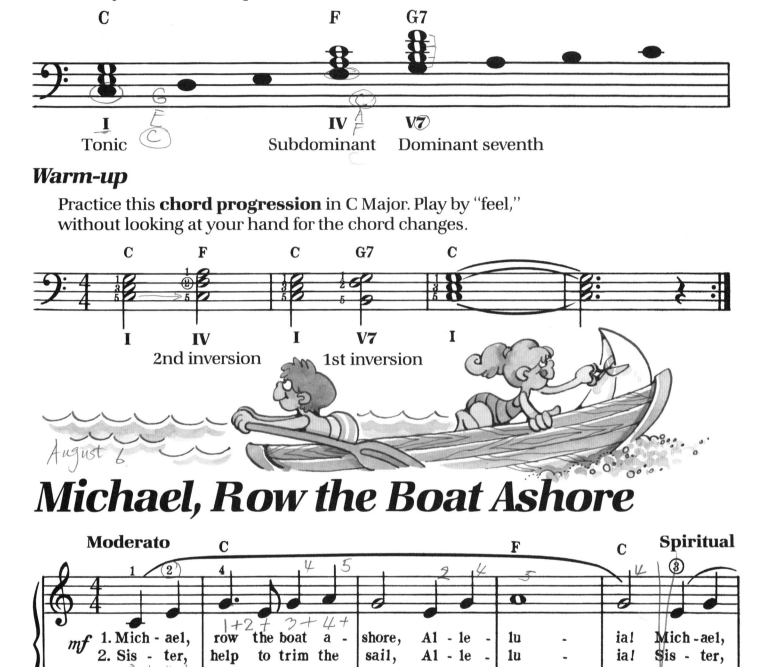

I — Tonic

IV — Subdominant

V7 — Dominant seventh

Warm-up

Practice this **chord progression** in C Major. Play by "feel,"
without looking at your hand for the chord changes.

I   IV   I   V7   I

2nd inversion   1st inversion

Michael, Row the Boat Ashore

Moderato   **Spiritual**

mf 1. Mich - ael, row the boat a - shore, Al - le - lu - ia! Mich-ael,
      2. Sis - ter, help to trim the sail, Al - le - lu - ia! Sis - ter,

row the boat a - shore, Al - le - lu - ia!
help to trim the sail, Al - le - lu - ia!

August 6

Lavender's Blue

Moderato

English Folk Song

mp Lav - en - der's blue, dil - ly, dil - ly, Lav - en - der's green,

When I am king, dil - ly, dil - ly, You shall be queen.

Who told you so, dil - ly, dil - ly, Who told you so?

'Twas my own heart, dil - ly, dil - ly, That told me so.

rit. slow down

Warm-up

R.H. plays I V7

The Marines' Hymn

March tempo

Warm-up

R.H. plays I IV V7

Kum-Ba-Ya*

Moderato

African Folk Hymn

August 13

Kum-ba-ya means come by here.

August 13. memorize.

G Major Scale

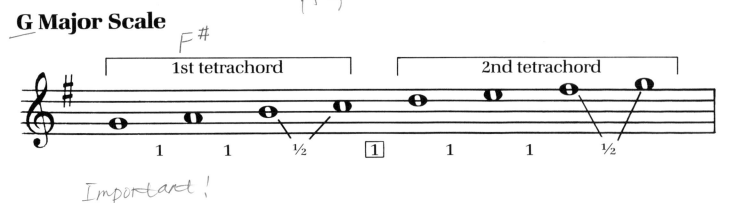

Play hands separately first.

Important!

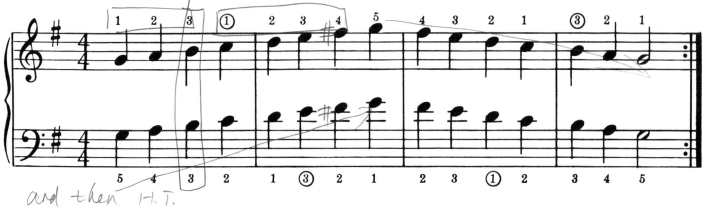

and then H.T.

Primary Chords in G Major

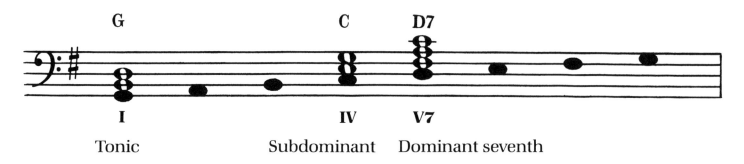

I	IV	V7
Tonic	Subdominant	Dominant seventh

Warm-up

Practice this **chord progression** in G Major. Play by "feel," without looking at your hands for the chord changes. Play hands separately first.

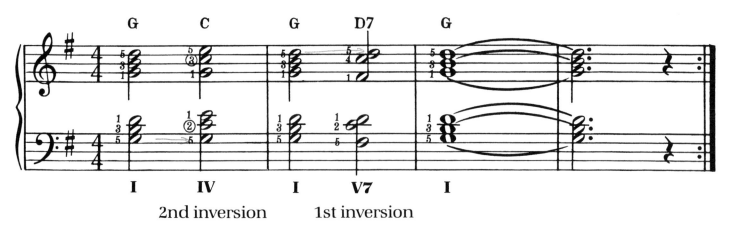

Old MacDonald Rocks

$C = \frac{4}{4}$

The sign C is another way of writing the $\frac{4}{4}$ time signature.
This time signature is called **common time**.

Olympic Games

Steady march tempo

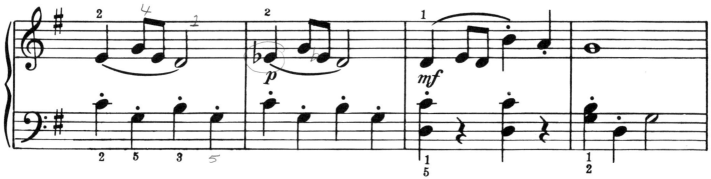

Section B

Section A

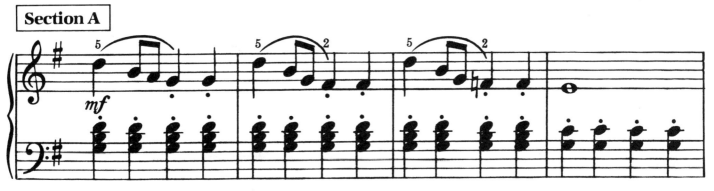

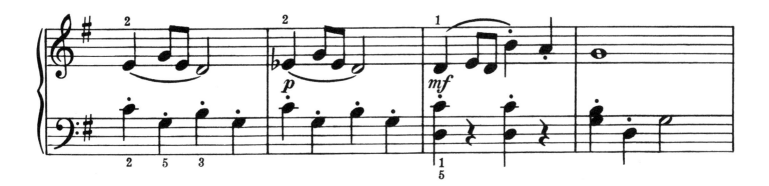

Coda*

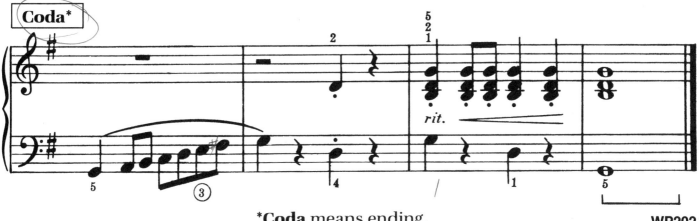

*Coda** means ending.

$\frac{6}{8}$ Time Signature

6 means six beats to each measure.
8 means the eighth note gets one beat.

Notes

Rests

1 beat

2 beats

3 beats

6 beats

Clap and count these rhythms.

Play the music below and count aloud.
Then transpose to C and F.

$\frac{6}{8}$ *Rhythm Study*

Moderato

f-p

New notes

Allegro

Tarantella*

Section A

Section B

D. C. al Fine

*A *tarantella* is a fast Italian dance. There used to be a superstition that the madness caused from the bite of a tarantula spider could only be cured by wild dancing.

Scottish Bagpipes

Fermata Sign

This sign ⌢ is called a **fermata**. It means to hold the note longer than the time value.

Sailing!

New note C

F Major Scale

key:
Bb

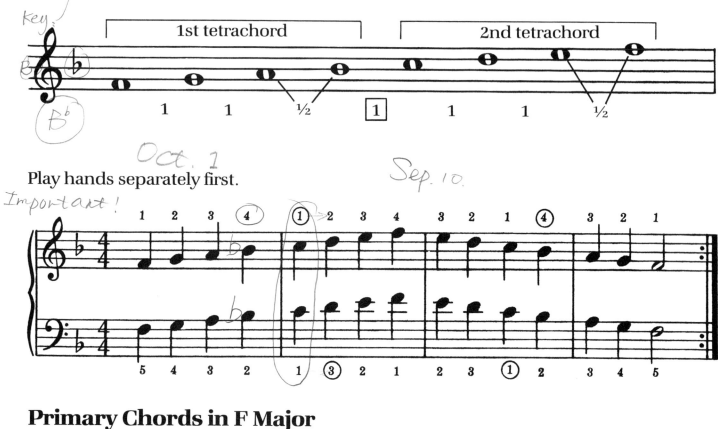

	1st tetrachord				2nd tetrachord		
1	1	½	[1]	1	1	½	

Oct. 1

Play hands separately first.

Sep. 10.

Important!

1 2 3 ④ ①→2 3 4 3 2 1 ④ 3 2 1
5 4 3 2 1 ③ 2 1 2 3 ① 2 3 4 5

Primary Chords in F Major

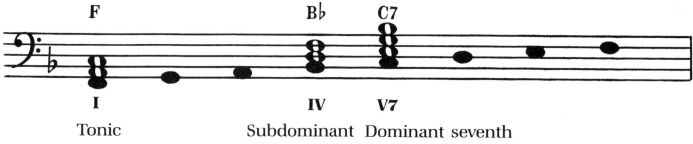

F   Bb   C7

I   IV   V7

Tonic   Subdominant Dominant seventh

Warm-up

Practice this **chord progression** in F Major. Play by "feel," without looking at your hands for the chord changes. Play hands separately first.

relax

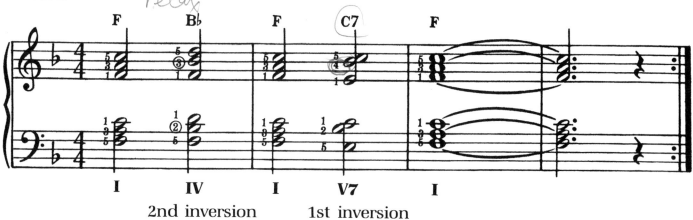

F   Bb   F   C7   F

I   IV   I   V7   I

2nd inversion   1st inversion

WP202

Can Can

Offenbach
(arranged)

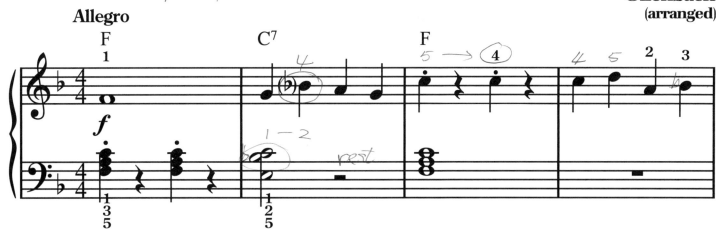

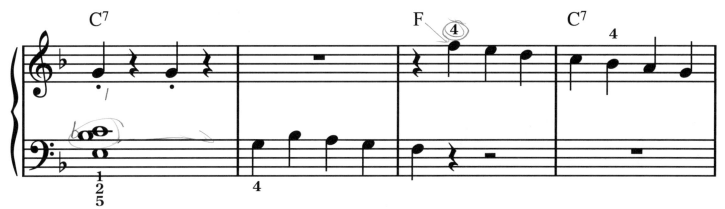

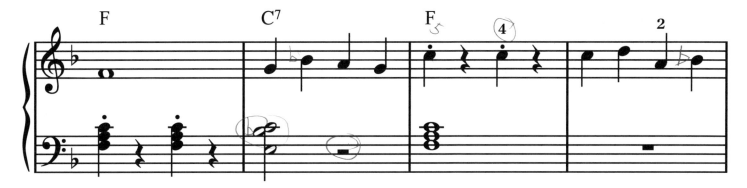

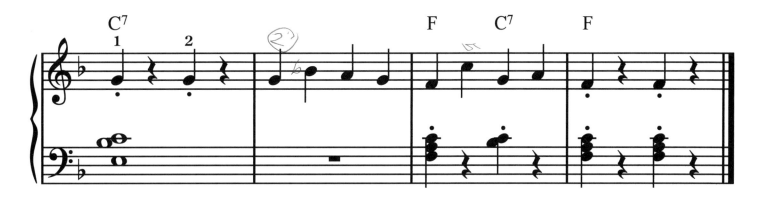

Roumanian Rhapsody

Workout in Space

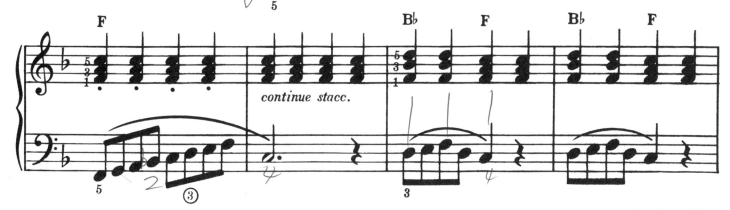

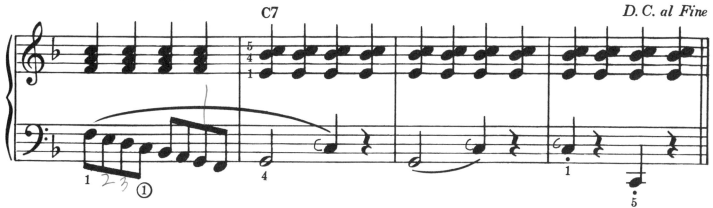

The Order of Sharps

The **sharps** are *always* written in the same order on the staff. **Memorize** this order.

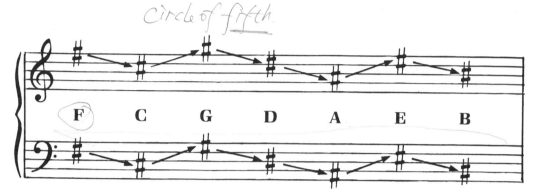

F   C   G   D   A   E   B

Write the order of sharps three times on this staff.*

Major Sharp Key Signatures

The **key signature** at the beginning of each staff tells you which notes to play sharp or flat **throughout** the piece, and the main tonality, or **key**, of the piece.

To find the **sharp** key signatures, name the *last sharp* to the right in the key signature. Then name the *next letter* in the music alphabet (go up a half step). This is the name of the Major key.

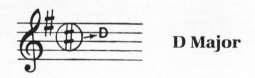   **D Major**

Name these key signatures.

—————— —————— —————— ——————

*Teacher: Continue to have the student use **Bastien Music Notebook** and **Bastien Music Flashcards** for reinforcement.

Group 2 Keys (D, A, E)

These keys are called **Group 2** because in each I (tonic) chord there is a **black key** in the **middle**.

D Major

A Major

E Major

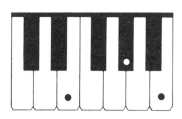

Warm-ups

Play these chords. Count aloud.

Key of D

Key of A

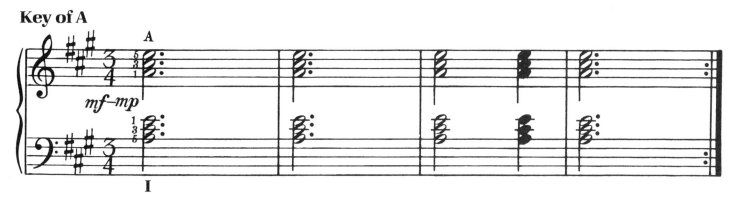

Key of E

D Major Scale

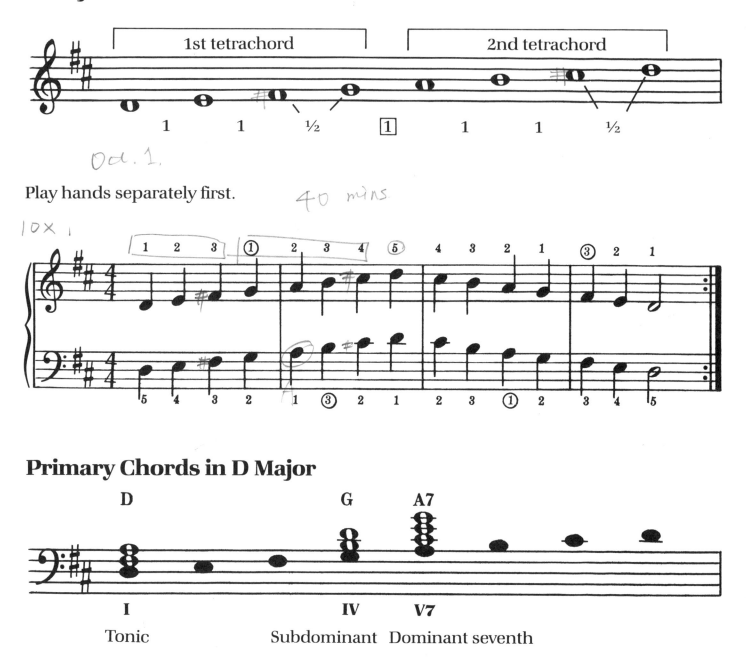

1st tetrachord   2nd tetrachord

1   1   ½   1   1   1   ½

Play hands separately first.

Primary Chords in D Major

D   G   A7

I   IV   V7

Tonic   Subdominant   Dominant seventh

Warm-up

Practice this **chord progression** in D Major. Play by "feel," without looking at your hands for the chord changes. Play hands separately first.

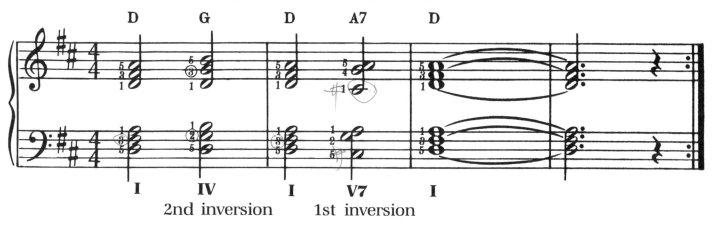

D   G   D   A7   D

I   IV   I   V7   I

2nd inversion   1st inversion

Warm-up

Play legato. Repeat, play staccato.

Play as written, then transpose to C, G, and F.

Down in the Valley

Moderato

mp

1. Down in the val - ley, val-ley so low,___ Hang your head
2. Hang your head o - ver, hear the wind blow,___ Hang your head

o - ver, hear the wind blow.___
o - ver, hear the wind blow.___

Is this piece in two-part, or three-part form?

Country Gardens

English Dance

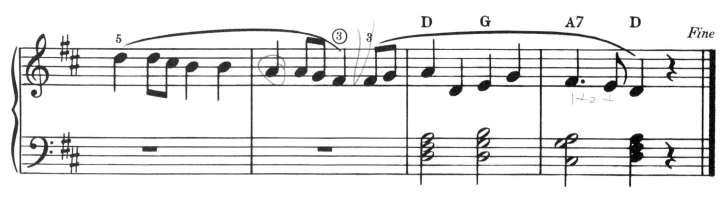

40 mins.

Is this piece in two-part, or three-part form?

Oct. 1.

Dancing the Minuet

Moderato

Fine

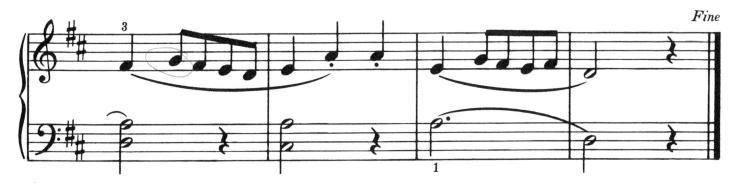

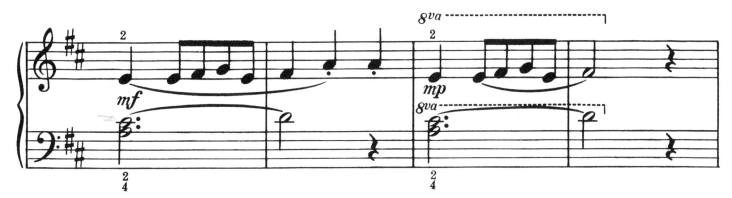

D.C. al Fine

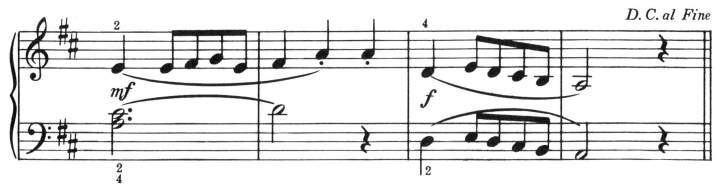

A Major Scale

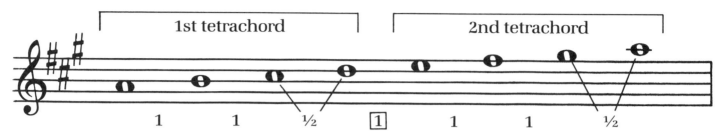

Play hands separately first.

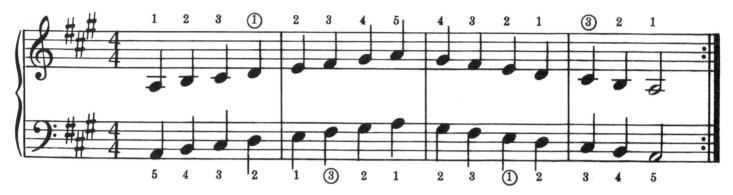

Primary Chords in A Major

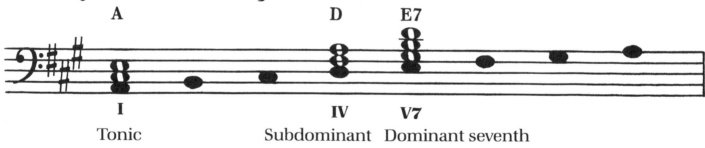

I   IV   V7

Tonic   Subdominant   Dominant seventh

Warm-up

Practice this **chord progression** in A Major. Play by "feel,"
without looking at your hands for the chord changes. Play
hands separately first.

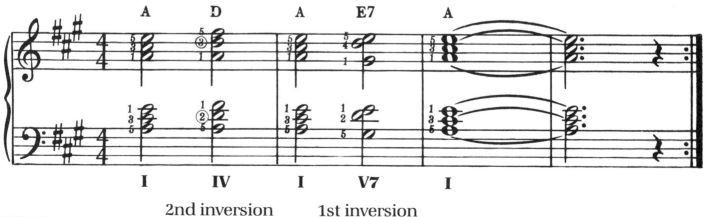

I   IV   I   V7   I

2nd inversion   1st inversion

Warm-up

Play legato. Repeat, play staccato.

Rockin' Rhythm!

Steady rock beat

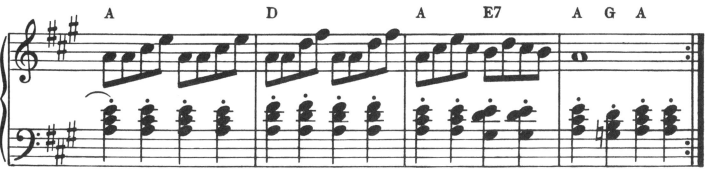

Wolfgang Amadeus Mozart (1756-1791) is one of the world's greatest composers. He was a very talented child and began composing at the age of five. Mozart performed his music throughout Europe, and today it is enjoyed by people all over the world.

The Mozart Family by de la Croce (1780-81).
Courtesy of the Salzburg Mozarteum.

Sonata Theme

Downhill Fun

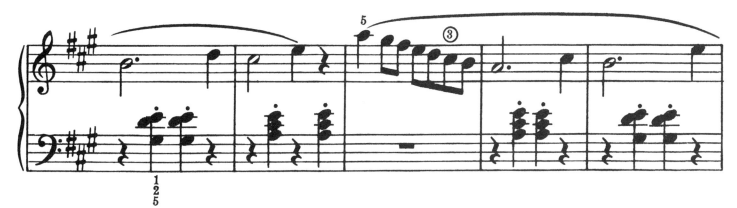

E Major Scale

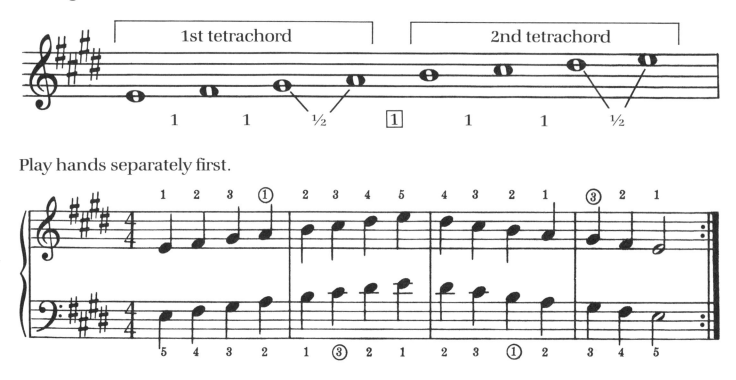

1st tetrachord   2nd tetrachord

1   1   ½   [1]   1   1   ½

Play hands separately first.

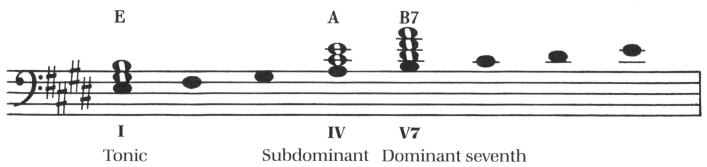

Primary Chords in E Major

E   A   B7

I   IV   V7

Tonic   Subdominant   Dominant seventh

Warm-up

Practice this **chord progression** in E Major. Play by "feel," without looking at your hands for the chord changes. Play hands separately first.

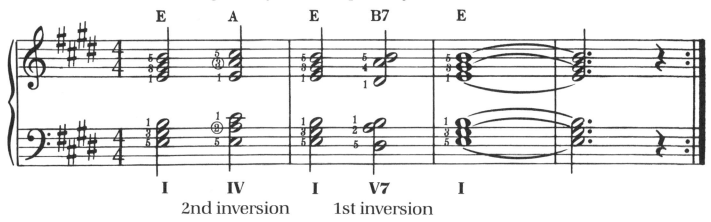

E   A   E   B7   E

I   IV   I   V7   I

2nd inversion   1st inversion

Warm-up
Play legato. Repeat, play staccato.

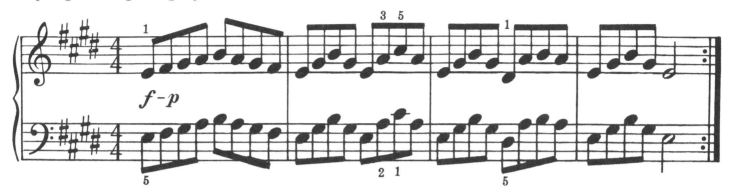

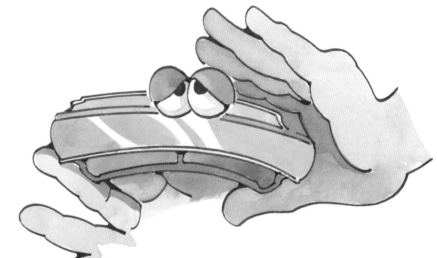

Blues in E
Fast!

Down by the Station

With spirit

mf

Down by the sta - tion

ear - ly in the morn - ing, See the lit - tle puf - fer bel - lies

all in a row. Lis-ten to them puff - ing, lis-ten to them

toot - ing. Puff, puff, toot, toot, off they go!

f

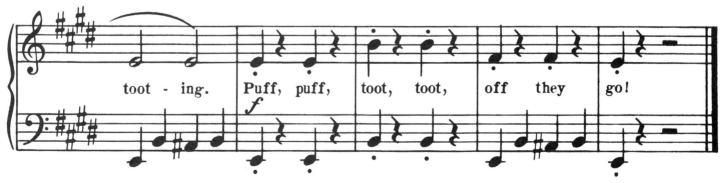

Barcarole*

Andante

Jacques Offenbach**
(1819-1880)

Section A

Section B

Section A

*A *barcarole* is a boat song of the gondoliers in Venice. The rhythm has
a lilt suggestive of the boat's movement in the water.

**Jacques Offenbach was a French composer who is best known for the many
short works he wrote for the musical theater.

The Entertainer

Scott Joplin *
(1868-1917)

Moderato

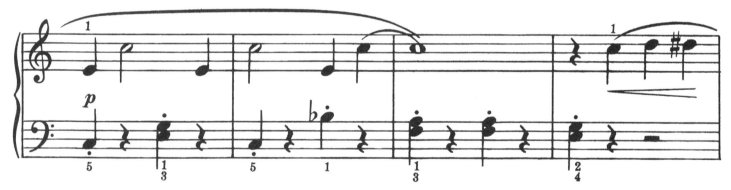

*Scott Joplin was an American composer who is best known for his popular music style known as ragtime.

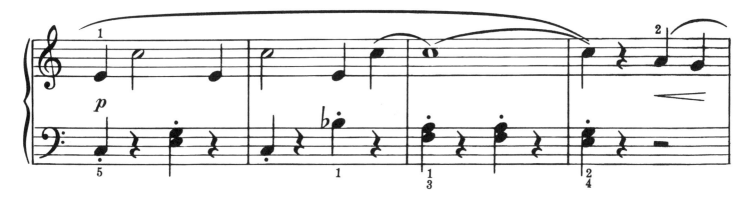

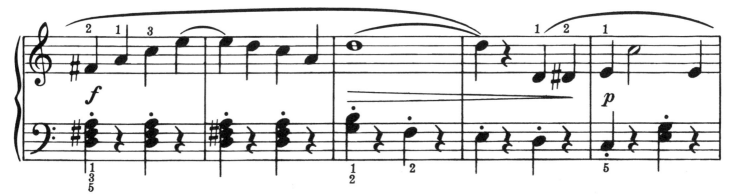

Music Review

1. Name these Major key signatures.

_____ _____   _____ _____ _____

2. Name these **harmonic** intervals.

_____ _____ _____ _____ _____ _____

3. Name these **melodic** intervals.

_____ _____ _____ _____ _____ _____

4. Write the whole (1) and half (½) steps for the G Major scale.

_____ _____ _____ _____ _____ _____

5. Write the counts for this rhythm.

_____

6. Write the Roman numerals for these primary chords in F Major.

_____ _____ _____ _____

Certificate
of Achievement

This certifies that

_____

has completed

Piano,
Level 2

of

Bastien Piano Basics

and is promoted to Level 3.

This certificate is given in recognition
of this significant achievement.

Date _____   Teacher _____